Prose Edda

ᚳᚱᚩᛋᛗ ᛗᚪᚪᚪᚠ

Otherwise known as the Younger Edda

Odin by: George Percy Jacob-Hood

Scribed by: Snorri Sturluson

Translated By: Benjamin Thorpe

Designed and Edited By:

Carrie Overton

Pocket Edda
Copyright © 2015 by Carrie Overton
Pocket Edda: Prose Edda
Copyright © 2015 by Carrie Overton
Pocket Edda: Younger Edda
Copyright © 2015 by Carrie Overton

Printed in the United States of America

First Edition 2015

ISBN: 978-1-937571-23-8

Library of Congress Control Number: 2015911985

Huginn and Muninn Publishing
1240 W Sims Way 93
Port Townsend, WA 98368

www.huginnandmuninn.net

CHAPTERS

GEFJON'S PLOUGHING.   7

GYLFI'S JOURNEY TO ASGARD.   7

OF THE SUPREME DEITY.   9

OF THE PRIMORDIAL STATE OF THE UNIVERSE.   10

ORIGIN OF THE HRIMTHURSAR, OR FROST-GIANTS.   10

OF THE COW AUDHUMLA, AND THE BIRTH OF ODIN.   12

HOW THE SONS OF BOR SLEW YMIR AND FROM HIS BODY
MADE HEAVEN AND EARTH.   12

OF THE FORMATION OF THE FIRST MAN AND WOMAN. 14

OF NIGHT AND DAY.   15

OF THE SUN AND MOON.   15

OF THE WOLVES THAT PURSUE THE SUN AND MOON.   16

OF THE WAY THAT LEADS TO HEAVEN.   17

THE GOLDEN AGE.   18

ORIGIN OF THE DWARFS.   18

OF THE ASH YGGDRASILL, MIMIR'S WELL, AND THE NORNS
OR DESTINIES.   19

OF THE VARIOUS CELESTIAL REGIONS.   22

OF THE WIND AND THE SEASONS.   23

OF ODIN.   23

OF THOR.   24

OF BALDUR.   25

OF NJORD.   26

OF THE GOD FREY, AND THE GODDESS FREYJA.   27

OF TYR. 27

OF THE OTHER GODS.   28

HODUR THE BLIND, ASSASSIN OF BALDUR   29

OF LOKI AND HIS PROGENY.   30

BINDING THE WOLF FENIR.   32

OF THE GODDESSES.   34

OF FREY AND GERDA.   36

OF THE JOYS OF VALHALLA.   38

OF THE HORSE SLEIPNIR.   41

OF THE SHIP SKIDBLADNIR.   43

THOR'S ADVENTURES ON HIS JOURNEY TO THE LAND OF THE GIANTS.   43

HOW THOR WENT TO FISH FOR THE MIDGARD SERPENT. 54

THE DEATH OF BALDUR THE GOOD.   56

BALDUR IN THE ABODE OF THE DEAD.   59

THE FLIGHT AND PUNISHMENT OF LOKI.   61

OF RAGNAROK, OR THE TWILIGHT OE THE GODS, AND THE CONFLAGRATION OF THE UNIVERSE.   63

OF THE ABODES OF FUTURE BLISS AND MISERY.   65

THE RENOVATION OF THE UNIVERSE.   66

ÆGIR'S JOURNEY TO ASGARD.   68

IDUNA AND HER APPLES.   68

THE ORIGIN OF POETRY.   70

ODIN BEGUILES THE DAUGHTER OF BAUGI   71

THE DELUDING OF GYLFI

GEFJON'S PLOUGHING. [125]

1. King Gylfi ruled over the land which is now called Svithiod (Sweden). It is related of him that he once gave a wayfaring woman, as a recompense for her having diverted him, as much land in his realm as she could plough with four oxen in a day and a night. This woman was, however, of the race of the Æsir, and was called Gefjon. She took four oxen from the north, out of Jotunheim (but they were the sons she had had with a giant), and set them before a plough. Now the plough made such deep furrows that it tore up the land, which the oxen drew westward out to sea until they came to a sound. There Gefjon fixed the land, and called it Sælund. And the place where the land had stood became water, and formed a lake which is now called "The Water" (Laugur), and the inlets of this lake correspond exactly with the headlands of Sealund. As Skald Bragi the Old saith:--

"Gefjon drew from Gylfi, Rich in stored up treasure, The land she joined to Denmark.   Four heads and eight eyes bearing,   While hot sweat trickled down them, The oxen dragged the reft mass   That formed this winsome island."

GYLFI'S JOURNEY TO ASGARD.

2. King Gylfi was renowned for his wisdom and skill in magic. He beheld with astonishment that whatever the Æsir willed took place; and was at a loss whether to attribute their success to the superiority of their natural abilities, or to a power imparted to them by the mighty gods whom they worshipped. To be satisfied in this particular, he resolved to go to Asgard,

and, taking upon himself the likeness of an old man, set out on his journey. But the Æsir, being too well skilled in divination not to foresee his design, prepared to receive him with various illusions. On entering the city Gylfi saw a very lofty mansion, the roof of which, as far as his eye could reach, was covered with golden shields. Thiodolf of Hvina thus alludes to Valhalla being roofed with shields.

"Warriors all care-worn, (Stones had poured upon them),   On their backs let glisten   Valhalla's golden shingles."

At the entrance of the mansion Gylfi saw a man who amused himself by tossing seven small-swords in the air, and catching them as they fell, one after the other. This person having asked his name, Gylfi said that he was called Gangler, and that he came from a long journey, and begged for a night's lodging. He asked, in his turn, to whom this mansion belonged. The other told him that it belonged to their king,

and added, "But I will lead thee to him, and thou shalt thyself ask him his name." So saying he entered the hall, and as Gylfi followed the door banged to behind him. He there saw many stately rooms crowded with people, some playing, some drinking, and others fighting with various weapons. Gangler, seeing a multitude of things, the meaning of which he could not comprehend, softly pronounced the following verse (from the Havamal, st. i.):--

"Scan every gate   Ere thou go on,   With greatest caution;

For hard to say 'tis Where foes are sitting   In this fair mansion."

He afterwards beheld three thrones raised one above another, with a man sitting on each of them. Upon his asking what the names of these lords might be, his guide answered: "He who sitteth on the lowest throne is a king; his name is Har (the High or Lofty One); the second is Jafnhar (_i.e._ equal to the High); but he who sitteth on the highest throne is called Thridi (the Third)." Har, perceiving the stranger, asked him what his errand was, adding that he should be welcome to eat and drink without cost, as were all those who remained in Hava Hall. Gangler said he desired first to ascertain whether there was any person present renowned for his wisdom.

"If thou art not the most knowing," replied Har, "I fear thou wilt hardly return safe. But go, stand there below, and propose thy questions, here sits one who will be able to answer them."

OF THE SUPREME DEITY.

3. Gangler thus began his discourse:--"'Who is the first, or eldest of the gods?"

"In our language," replied Har, "he is called Alfadir (All-Father, or the Father of all); but in the old Asgard he had twelve names."

"Where is this God?" said Gangler; "what is his power? and what hath he done to display his glory?"

"He liveth," replied Har, "from all ages, he governeth all realms and swayeth all things great and small."

"He hath formed," added Jafnhar, "heaven and earth, and the air, and all things thereunto belonging."

"And what is more," continued Thridi, "he hath made man, and given him a soul which shall live and never perish though the body shall have mouldered away, or have been burnt to ashes. And all that are righteous shall dwell with him in the place called Gimli, or Vingolf; but the wicked shall go to Hel, and thence to Niflhel, which is below, in the ninth world."

"And where did this god remain before he made heaven and earth?" demanded Gangler.

"He was then," replied Har, "with the Hrimthursar."[126]

OF THE PRIMORDIAL STATE OF THE UNIVERSE.

4. "But with what did he begin, or what was the beginning of things?" demanded Gangler.

"Hear," replied Har, "what is said in the Voluspa."

"'Twas time's first dawn, When nought yet was,   Nor sand nor sea,   Nor cooling wave;   Earth was not there,

Nor heaven above. Nought save a void   And yawning gulf.   But verdure none.'"

"Many ages before the earth was made," added Jafnhar, "was Niflheim formed, in the middle of which lies the spring called Hvergelmir, from which flow twelve rivers, Gjoll being the nearest to the gate of the abode of death."

"But, first of all," continued Thridi, "there was in the southern region (sphere) the world called Muspell. It is a world too luminous and glowing to be entered by those who are not indigenous there.[127] He who sitteth on its borders (or the land's-end) to guard it is named Surtur. In his hand he beareth a flaming falchion, and at the end of the world shall issue forth to combat, and shall vanquish all the gods, and consume the universe with fire."

ORIGIN OF THE HRIMTHURSAR, OR FROST-GIANTS.

5. "Tell me," said Gangler, "what was the state of things ere the races mingled, and nations came into being."

"When the rivers that are called Elivagar had flowed far from their sources," replied Har, "the venom which they rolled along hardened, as does dross that runs from a furnace, and became ice.

When the rivers flowed no longer, and the ice stood still, the vapour arising from the venom gathered over it, and froze to rime, and in this manner were formed, in Ginnungagap, many layers of congealed vapour, piled one over the other."

"That part of Ginnungagap," added Jafnhar, "that lies towards the north was thus filled with heavy masses of gelid vapour and ice, whilst everywhere within were whirlwinds and fleeting mists. But the southern part of Ginnungagap was lighted by the sparks and flakes that flew into it from Muspellheim."

"Thus," continued Thridi, "whilst freezing cold and gathering gloom proceeded from Niflheim, that part of Ginnungagap looking towards Muspellheim was filled with glowing radiancy, the intervening space remaining calm and light as wind-still air. And when the heated blast met the gelid vapour it melted it into drops, and, by the might of him who sent the heat, these drops quickened into life, and

took a human semblance. The being thus formed was named Ymir, but the Frost-giants call him Orgelmir. From him descend the race of the Frost-giants (Hrimthursar), as it is said in the Voluspa, 'From Vidolf come all witches; from Vilmeith all wizards; from Svarthofdi all poison-seethers; and all giants from Ymir.' And the giant Vafthrûdnir, when Gangrad asked, 'Whence came Orgelmir the first of the sons of giants?' answered, 'The Elivagar cast out drops of venom that quickened into a giant. From him spring all our race, and hence are we so strong and mighty.'"

"How did the race of Ymir spread itself?" asked Gangler; "or dost thou believe that this giant was a god?"

"We are far from believing him to have been a god," replied Har, "for he was wicked as are all of his race, whom we call Frost-giants. And it is said that, when Ymir slept, he fell into a sweat, and from the pit of his left arm was born a man and a woman, and one of his feet engendered with the other a son, from whom descend the Frost-giants, and we therefore call Ymir the old Frost-giant."

OF THE COW AUDHUM-LA, AND THE BIRTH OF ODIN.

6. "Where dwelt Ymir, and on what did he live?" asked Gangler.

"Immediately after the gelid vapours had been resolved into drops," replied Kar, "there was formed out of them the cow named Aud-humla. Four streams of milk ran from her teats, and thus fed she Ymir."

"But on what did the cow feed?" questioned Gangler.

"The cow," answered Har, "supported herself by licking the stones that were covered with salt and hoar frost. The first day that she licked these stones there sprang from them, towards evening, the

hairs of a man, the second day a head, and on the third an entire man, who was endowed with beauty, agility and power. He was called Bur, and was the father of Bor, who took for his wife Besla, the daughter of the giant Bolthorn. And they had three sons, Odin, Vili, and Ve; and it is our belief that this Odin, with his brothers, ruleth both heaven and earth, and that Odin is his true name, and that he is the most mighty of all the gods."

HOW THE SONS OF BOR SLEW YMIR AND FROM HIS BODY MADE HEAV-EN AND EARTH.

7. "Was there," asked Gangler, "any kind of equality or any degree of good understanding between these two races?"

"Far from it," replied Har; "for the sons of Bor slew the giant Ymir, and when he fell there ran so much blood from his wounds, that the whole race of Frost-giants was drowned in it, except a single giant, who saved himself with his household. He is called by the giants Bergelmir. He escaped by going on board his bark, and with him went his wife, and from them are descended the Frost-giants."

8. "And what became of the sons of Bor, whom ye look upon as gods?" asked Gangler.

"To relate this," replied Har, "is no trivial matter. They dragged the body of Ymir into the middle of Ginnungagap, and of it formed the earth. From Ymir's blood they made the seas and waters; from his flesh the land; from his bones the mountains; and his teeth and jaws, together with some bits of broken bones, served them to make the stones and pebbles."

"With the blood that ran from his wounds," added Jafnhar, "they made the vast ocean, in the midst of which they fixed the earth, the ocean encircling it as a ring, and hardy will he be who attempts to pass those waters."

"From his skull," continued Thridi, "they formed the heavens, which they placed over the earth, and set a dwarf at the corner of each of the four quarters. These dwarfs are called East, West, North, and South. They afterwards took the wandering sparks and red hot flakes that had been cast out of Muspellheim, and placed them in the heavens, both above and below, to' give light unto the world, and assigned to every other errant coruscation a prescribed locality and motion. Hence it is recorded in ancient lore that from this time were marked out the days, and nights, and seasons."

"Such are the events that took place ere the earth obtained the form it now beareth."

"Truly great were the deeds ye tell me of!" exclaimed Gangler; "and wondrous in all its parts is the work thereby accomplished. But how is the earth fashioned?"

"It is round without," replied Har, "and encircled by the deep ocean, the outward shores of which were assigned for a dwelling to the race of giants. But within, round about the earth, they (the sons of Bor) raised a bulwark against turbulent giants, employing for this structure Ymir's eyebrows. To this bulwark they gave the name of Midgard[128] They afterwards tossed Ymir's brains into the air, and they became the clouds, for thus we find it recorded.

"Of Ymir's flesh was formed the earth; of his sweat (blood), the seas; of his bones, the mountains; of his hair the trees; of his skull, the heavens; but with his eyebrows the blithe gods built Midgard for the sons of men, whilst from his brains the lowering clouds were fashioned."

OF THE FORMATION OF THE FIRST MAN AND WOMAN.

9. "To make heaven and earth, to fix the sun and the moon in the firmament, and mark out the days and seasons, were, indeed, important labours." said Gangler; "but whence came the men who at present dwell in the world?"

"One day." replied Har, "as the sons of Bor were walking along the sea-beach they found two stems of wood, out of which they shaped a man and a woman. The first (Odin) infused into them life and spirit; the second (Vili) endowed them with reason and the power of motion; the third (Ve) gave them speech and features, hearing and vision. The man they called Ask, and the woman, Embla. From these two descend the whole human race whose assigned dwelling was within Midgard. Then the sons of Bor built in the middle of the universe the city called Asgard, where dwell the gods and their kindred, and from that abode work out so many wondrous things, both on the earth and in the heavens above it. There is in that city a place called Hlidskjalf, and when Odin is seated there on his lofty throne he sees over the whole world, discerns all the actions of men, and comprehends whatever he contemplates. His wife is Frigga, the daughter of Fjorgyn, and they and their offspring form the race that we call Æsir, a race that dwells in Asgard the old, and the regions around it, and that we know to be entirely divine. Wherefore Odin may justly be called All-father, for he is verily the father of all, of gods as well as of men, and to his power all things owe their existence. Earth is his daughter and his wife, and with her he had his first-born son, Asa-Thor, who is endowed with strength and valour, and therefore quelleth he everything that hath life."

OF NIGHT AND DAY.

10. "A giant called Njorvi," continued Har, "who dwelt in Jotunheim, had a daughter called Night (Nott) who, like all her race, was of a dark and swarthy complexion. She was first wedded to a man called Naglfari, and had by him a son named Aud, and afterwards to another man called Annar, by whom she had a daughter called Earth (Jord). She then espoused Delling, of the Æsir race, and their son was Day, (Dagr) a child light and beauteous like his father. Then took All-father, Night, and Day, her son, and gave them two horses and two cars, and set them up in the heavens that they might drive successively one after the other, each in twelve hours' time, round the world. Night rides first on her horse called Hrimfaxi, that every morn, as he ends his course, bedews the earth with the foam that falls from his bit. The horse made use of by Day is named Skinfaxi, from whose mane is shed light over the earth and the heavens."

OF THE SUN AND MOON.

11. "How doth All-father regulate the course of the sun and moon?" asked Gangler.

"There was formerly a man," replied Har, "named Mundil-fari, who had two children so lovely and graceful that he called the male, Mani (moon), and the female, Sol (sun), who espoused the man named Glenur. But the gods being incensed at Mundilfari's presumption, took his children and placed them in the heavens, and let Sol drive the horses that draw the car of the sun, which the gods had made to give light to the world out of the sparks that flew from Muspellheim. These horses are called Arvak and Alsvid, and under their withers the gods placed two skins filled with air to cool and refresh them, or, according to some ancient traditions, a refrigerant substance called _isarn-kul_.[129] Mani was set to guide the moon in his course, and regulate his increasing and waning aspect. One day he carried off from the earth two children, named Bil and Hjuki, as they were returning from the spring called Byrgir, carrying between them the bucket called Saegr, on the pole Simul. Vidfinn was the father of these children, who always follow Mani (the moon), as we may easily observe even from the earth."

OF THE WOLVES THAT PURSUE THE SUN AND MOON.

12. "But the sun," said Gangler, speeds at such a rate as if she feared that some one was pursuing her for her destruction."

"And well she may," replied Har, "for he that seeks her is not far behind, and she has no way to escape than to run before him."

"But who is he," asked Gangler, "that causes her this anxiety?"

"There are two wolves," answered Har; "the one called Skoll pursues the sun, and it is he that she fears, for he shall one day overtake and devour her; the other, called Hati, the son of Hrodvitnir, runs before her, and as eagerly pursues the moon that will one day be caught by him."

"Whence come these wolves?" asked Gangler.

"A hag," replied Har, "dwells in a wood, to the eastward of Midgard, called Jarnvid, (the Iron Wood,) which is the abode of a race of witches called Jarnvidjur. This old hag is the mother of many gigantic sons, who are all of them shaped like wolves, two of whom are the wolves thou askest about. There is one of that race, who is said to be the most formidable of all, called Managarm: he will be filled with the life-blood of men who draw near their end, and will swallow up the moon, and stain the heavens and the earth with blood. Then shall the sun grow dim, and the winds howl tumultuously to and fro."

OF THE WAY THAT LEADS TO HEAVEN.

13. "I must now ask," said Gangler, "which is the path leading from earth to heaven?"

"That is a senseless question," replied Har, with a smile of derision. "Hast thou not been told that the gods made a bridge from earth to heaven, and called it Bifrost? Thou must surely have seen it; but, perhaps, thou callest it the rainbow. It is of three hues, and is constructed with more art than any other work. But, strong though it be, it will be broken to pieces when the sons of Muspell, after having traversed great rivers, shall ride over it."

"Methinks," said Gangler, "the gods could not have been in earnest to erect a bridge so liable to be broken down, since it is in their power to make whatever they please."

"The gods," replied Har, "are not to be blamed on that account; Bifrost is of itself a very good bridge, but there is nothing in nature that can hope to make resistance when the sons of Muspell sally forth to the great combat."

THE GOLDEN AGE.

14. "What did All-father do after Asgard was made?" demanded Gangler.

"In the beginning," answered Har, "he appointed rulers, and bade them judge with him the fate of men, and regulate the government of the celestial city. They met for this purpose in a place called Idavoll, which is in the centre of the divine abode. Their first work was to erect a court or hall wherein are twelve seats for themselves, besides the throne which is occupied by All-father. This hall is the largest and most magnificent in the universe, being resplendent on all sides, both within and without, with the finest gold. Its name is Gladsheim. They also erected another hall for the sanctuary of the goddesses. It is a very fair structure, and called by men Vingolf. Lastly they built a smithy, and furnished it with hammers, tongs, and anvils, and with these made all the other requisite instruments, with which they worked in metal, stone and wood, and composed so large a quantity of the metal called gold that they made all their moveables of it. Hence that age was named the Golden Age. This was the age that lasted until the arrival of the women out of Jotunheim, who corrupted it."

ORIGIN OF THE DWARFS.

15. "Then the gods, seating themselves upon their thrones, distributed justice, and bethought them how the dwarfs had been bred in the mould of the earth, just as worms are in a dead body. It was, in fact, in Ymir's flesh that the dwarfs were engendered, and began to move and live. At first they were only maggots, but by the will of the gods they at length partook both of human shape and understanding, although they always dwell in rocks and caverns.

"Modsognir and Durin are the principal ones. As it is said in the Voluspa--

"'Then went the rulers there,   All gods most holy,   To their seats aloft, And counsel together took, Who should of dwarfs   The race then fashion,   From the livid bones   And blood of the giant.

Modsognir, chief   Of the dwarfish race,   And Durin too   Were then created. And like to men   Dwarfs in the earth   Were formed in numbers   As Durin ordered.'"

OF THE ASH YGG-DRASILL, MIMIR'S WELL., AND THE NORNS OR DESTINIES.

16. "Where," asked Gangler, "is the chief or holiest seat of the gods?"

"It is under the ash Ygg-drasill," replied Har, "where the gods assemble every day in council."

"What is there remarkable in regard to that place?" said Gangler.

"That ash," answered Jafnhar, "is the greatest and best of all trees. Its branches spread over the whole world, and even reach above heaven. It has three roots very wide asunder. One of them extends to the Æsir, another to the Frost-giants in that very place where was formerly Ginnun-gagap, and the third stands over Nifelheim, and under this root, which is constant-ly gnawed by Nidhogg, is Hvergelmir. But under the root that stretches out towards the Frost-giants there is Mimir's well, in which wis-dom and wit lie hidden. The owner of this well is called Mimir. He is full of wisdom, because he drinks the waters of the well from the horn Gjoll every morning. One day All-father came and begged a draught of this water, which he obtained, but was obliged to leave one of his eyes as a pledge for it.

"The third root of the ash is in heaven, and under it is the holy Urdar fount. 'Tis here that the gods sit in judgment. Every day they ride up hither on horseback over Bifrost, which is called the Æsir Bridge. These are the names of the horses of the Æsir. Sleipnir is the best of them; he has eight legs, and belongs to Odin. The others are Gladr, Gyllir, Glær, Skeidbrimir, Silfrintoppr, Synir, Gils, Falhofnir, Gulltoppr, and Lettfeti. Baldur's horse was burnt with his master's body. As for Thor, he goes on foot, and is obliged every day to wade the rivers called Kormt and OErmt, and two others called Kerlaung.

"Through these shall Thor wade every day, as he fares to the doomstead under Yggdrasill's ash, else the Æsir Bridge would be in flames, and boiling hot would become the holy waters."[130] "But tell me," said Gangler, "does fire burn over Bifrost?"

"That," replied Har, "which thou seest red in the bow, is burning fire; for the Frost-giants and the Mountain-giants would go up to heaven by that bridge if it were easy for every one to walk over it. There are in heaven many goodly homesteads, and none without a celestial ward. Near the fountain, which is under the ash, stands a very beauteous dwelling, out of which go three maidens, named Urd, Verdandi, and Skuld.[131] These maidens fix the lifetime of all men, and are called Norns. But there are, indeed, many other Norns, for, when a man is born, there is a Norn to determine his fate. Some are known to be of heavenly origin, but others belong to the races of the elves and dwarfs; as it is said--

"'Methinks the Norns were born far asunder, for they are not of the same race. Some belong to the Æsir, some to the Elves, and some are Dvalin's daughters.'

"But if these Norns dispense the destinies of men," said Gangler, "they are, methinks, very unequal in their distribution; for some men are fortunate and wealthy, others acquire neither riches nor honours, some live to a good old age, while others are cut off in their prime."

"The Norns," replied Har, "who are of a good origin, are good themselves, and dispense good destinies. But those men to whom misfortunes happen ought to ascribe them to the evil Norns."

17. "What more wonders hast thou to tell me," said Gangler, "concerning the ash?"

"What I have further to say respecting it," replied Har, "is, that there is an eagle perched upon its branches who knows many things: between his eyes sits the hawk called Vedurfolnir. The squirrel named Ratatosk runs up and down the ash, and seeks to cause strife between the eagle and Nidhogg. Four harts run across the branches of the tree, and bite the buds. They are called Dainn, Divalinn, Duneyr, and Durathror. But there are so many snakes with Nidhogg in Hvergelmir that no tongue can recount them."

"It is also said that the Norns who dwell by the Urdar-fount draw every day water from the spring, and with it and the clay that lies around the fount sprinkle the ash, in order that its branches may not rot and wither away. This water is so holy that everything placed in the spring becomes as white as the film, within an eggshell. As it is said in the Voluspa--

"'An Ash know I standing, Named Yggdrasill, A stately tree sprinkled With water the purest;

Thence come the dewdrops That fall in the dales; Ever blooming, it stands O'er the Urdar-fountain.'"

"The dew that falls thence on the earth men call honey-dew, and it is the food of the bees. Two fowls are fed in the Urdar-fount; they are called swans, and from them are descended all the birds of this species."

OF THE VARIOUS

CELESTIAL REGIONS.

18. "Thou tellest me many wonderful things of heaven," said Gangler, "but what other homesteads are to be seen there?"

"There are many other fair homesteads there," replied Har; "one of them is named Elf-home (Alfheim), wherein dwell the beings called the Elves of Light; but the Elves of Darkness live under the earth, and differ from the others still more in their actions than in their appearance. The Elves of Light are fairer than the sun, but the Elves of Darkness blacker than pitch. There is also a mansion called Breidablik, which is not inferior to any other in beauty; and another named Glitnir, the wall, columns and beams of which are of ruddy gold, and the roof of silver. There is also the stead called Himinbjorg, that stands on the borders where Bifrost touches heaven, and the

stately mansion belonging to Odin, called Valaskjalf, which was built by the gods, and roofed with pure silver, and in which is the throne called Hlidskjalf. When All-father is seated on this throne, he can see over the whole world. On the southern edge of heaven is the most beautiful homestead of all, brighter than the sun itself. It is called Gimli, and shall stand when both heaven and earth have passed away, and good and righteous men shall dwell therein for everlasting ages."

"But what will preserve this abode when Surtur's fire consumes heaven and earth?" asked Gangler.

"We are told," replied Har, "that towards the south there is another heaven above this called Andlang, and again above this a third heaven called Vidblain. In this last, we think Gimli must be seated, but we deem that the Elves of Light abide in it now."

OF THE WIND AND THE SEASONS.

19. "Tell me," said Gangler, "whence comes the wind, which is so strong that it moves the ocean and fans fire to flame, yet, strong though it be, no mortal eye can discern it? wonderfully, therefore, must it be shapen."

"I can tell thee all about it," answered Har; "thou must know that at the northern extremity of the heavens sits a giant called Hræsvelgur, clad with eagles' plumes. When he spreads out his wings for flight, the winds arise from under them."

20. "Tell me further," said Gangler, "why the summer should be hot, and the winter cold."

"A wise man would not ask such a question, which every one could answer," replied Har; "but, if thou hast been so dull as not to have heard the reason, I will rather forgive thee for once asking a foolish question than suffer thee to remain any longer in ignorance of what ought to have been known to thee. The father of Summer is called Svasuth, who is such a gentle and delicate being that what is mild is from him called sweet. The father of Winter has two names, Vindloni and Vindsval. He is the son of Vasad, and, like all his race, has an icy breath, and is of a grim and gloomy aspect."

OF ODIN.

21. "I must now ask thee," said Gangler, "who are the gods that men are bound to believe in?"

"There are twelve gods," replied Har, "to whom divine honours ought to be rendered."

"Nor are the goddesses," added Jafnhar, "less divine and mighty."

"The first and eldest of the Æsir," continued Thridi, "is Odin. He governs all things, and, although the other deities are powerful,

23

they all serve and obey him as children do their father. Frigga is his wife. She foresees the destinies of men, but never reveals what is to come. For thus it is said that Odin himself told Loki, 'Senseless Loki, why wilt thou pry into futurity, Frigga alone knoweth the destinies of all, though she telleth them never?'

"Odin is named Alfadir (All-father), because he is the father of all the gods, and also Valfadir (Choosing Father), because he chooses for his sons all of those who fall in combat. For their abode he has prepared Valhalla and Vingolf, where they are called Einherjar (Heroes or Champions). Odin is also called Hangagud, Haptagud, and Farmagud, and, besides these, was named in many ways when he went to King Geirraudr," forty-nine names in all.

"A great many names, indeed!" exclaimed Gangler; "surely that man must be very wise who knows them all distinctly, and can tell on what occasions they were given."

"It requires, no doubt," replied Har, "a good memory to recollect readily all these names, but I will tell thee in a few words what principally contributed to confer them upon him. It was the great variety of languages; for the various nations were obliged to translate his name into their respective tongues, in order that they might supplicate and worship him. Some of his names, however, have been owing to adventures that happened to him on his journeys, and which are related in old stories. Nor canst thou ever pass for a wise man if thou are not able to give an account of these wonderful adventures."

OF THOR.

22. "I now ask thee," said Gangler, "what are the names of the other gods. What are their functions, and what have they brought to pass?"

"The mightiest of them." replied Har, "is Thor. He is called Asa-Thor and Auku-Thor, and is the strongest of gods and men. His realm is named Thrudvang, and his mansion Bilskirnir, in which are five hundred and forty halls. It is the largest house ever built."

"Thor has a car drawn by two goats called Tanngniost and Tanngrisnir. From his driving about in this car he is called Auku-Thor (Charioteer-Thor). He likewise possesses three very precious things. The first is a mallet called Mjolnir, which both the Frost and Mountain Giants know to their cost when they see it hurled against them in the air; and no wonder, for it has split many a skull of their fathers and kindred. The second rare thing he possesses is called the belt of strength or prowess (Megingjardir). When he girds it about him his divine might is doubly augmented; the third, also very precious, being his iron gauntlets, which he is obliged to put on whenever he would lay hold of the handle of his mallet. There is no one so wise as to be able to relate all Thor's marvellous exploits, yet I could tell thee so many myself that hours would be whiled away ere all that I know had been recounted."

OF BALDUR.

23. "I would rather," said Gangler, "hear something about the other Æsir.»

"The second son of Odin," replied Har, "is Baldur, and it may be truly said of him that he is the best, and that all mankind are loud in his praise. So fair and dazzling is he in form and features, that rays of light seem to issue from him; and thou mayst have some idea of the beauty of his hair, when I tell thee that the whitest of all plants is called Baldur's brow. Baldur is the mildest, the wisest, and the most eloquent of all the Æsir, yet such is his nature that the judgment he has pronounced can never be altered. He dwells in the heavenly mansion called Breidablik, in which nothing unclean can enter."

OF NJORD.

24. "The third god," continued Har, "is Njord, who dwells in the heavenly region called Noatun. He rules over the winds, and checks the fury of the sea and of fire, and is therefore invoked by sea-farers and fishermen. He is so wealthy that he can give possessions and treasures to those who call on him for them. Yet Njord is not of the lineage of the Æsir, for he was born and bred in Vanaheim. But the Vanir gave him as hostage to the Æsir, receiving from them in his stead Hoenir. By this means was peace re-established between the Æsir and Vanir. Njord took to wife Skadi, the daughter of the giant Thjassi. She preferred dwelling in the abode formerly belonging to her father, which is situated among rocky mountains, in the region called Thrymheim, but Njord loved to reside near the sea. They at last agreed that they should pass together nine nights in Thrymheim, and then three in Noatun.

One day, when Njord came back from the mountains to Noatun, he thus sang--

"'Of mountains I'm weary, Not long was I there, Not more than nine nights;

But the howl of the wolf Methought sounded ill To the song of the swan-bird.'

"To which Skadi sang in reply--

"'Ne'er can I sleep In my couch on the strand, For the screams of the sea-fowl, The mew as he comes Every morn from the main Is sure to awake me.'

"Skadi then returned to the rocky mountains, and abode in Thrymheim. There, fastening on her snow-skates and taking her bow, she passes her time in the chase of savage beasts, and is called the Ondur goddess, or Ondurdis. As it is said--

"'Thrymheim's the land
Where Thjassi abode   That
mightiest of giants.   But
snow-skating Skadi   Now
dwells there, I trow,   In her
father's old mansion.'"

OF THE GOD FREY, AND
THE GODDESS FREYJA.

25. "Njord had afterwards, at
his residence at Noatun, two
children, a son named Frey,
and a daughter called Freyja,
both of them beauteous and
mighty. Frey is one of the
most celebrated of the gods.
He presides over rain and
sunshine, and all the fruits
of the earth, and should be
invoked in order to obtain
good harvests, and also
for peace. He, moreover,
dispenses wealth among men.
Freyja is the most propitious
of the goddesses; her abode
in heaven is called Folkvang.
To whatever field of battle she
rides, she asserts her right to
one half of the slain, the other
half belonging to Odin. As it
is said--

"'Folkvang 'tis called
Where Freyja hath right to
dispose of the hall seats

Every day of the slain,
She chooseth the half, And
half leaves to Odin.'

"Her mansion, called Sess-
rumnir, is large and magnificent; thence she sallies forth
in a car drawn by two cats.
She lends a very favourable
ear to those who sue to her
for assistance. It is from her
name that women of birth
and fortune are called in
our language Freyjor. She is
very fond of love ditties, and
all lovers would do well to
invoke her."

OF TYR.

26. "All the gods appear to
me," said Gangler, "to have
great power, and I am not at
all surprised that ye are able
to perform so many great
achievements, since ye are
so well acquainted with the
attributes and functions of
each god, and know what is
befitting to ask from each, in
order to succeed.

But are there any more of them besides those you have already mentioned?"

"Ay," answered Har, "there is Tyr, who is the most daring and intrepid of all the gods. 'Tis he who dispenses valour in war, hence warriors do well to invoke him. It has become proverbial to say of a man who surpasses all others in valour that he is _Tyr-strong_, or valiant as Tyr. A man noted for his wisdom is also said to be 'wise as Tyr.' Let me give thee a proof of his intrepidity. When the Æsir were trying to persuade the wolf, Fenrir, to let himself be bound up with the chain, Gleipnir, he, fearing that they would never afterwards unloose him, only consented on the condition that while they were chaining him he should keep Tyr's right hand between his jaws. Tyr did not hesitate to put his hand in the monster's mouth, but when Fenrir perceived that the Æsir had no intention to unchain him, he bit the hand off at that point, which has ever since been called the wolf's joint. From that time Tyr has had but one hand. He is not regarded as a peacemaker among men."

OF THE OTHER GODS.

27. "There is another god," continued Har, "named Bragi, who is celebrated for his wisdom, and more especially for his eloquence and correct forms of speech. He is not only eminently skilled in poetry, but the art itself is called from his name _Bragr_, which epithet is also applied to denote a distinguished poet or poetess. His wife is named Iduna. She keeps in a box the apples which the gods, when they feel old age approaching, have only to taste of to become young again. It is in this manner that they will be kept in renovated youth until Ragnarok."

"Methinks," interrupted Gangler, "the gods have committed a great treasure to the guardianship and good faith of Iduna."

"And hence it happened," replied Har, smiling, "that they once ran the greatest risk

28

imaginable, as I shall have occasion to tell thee when thou hast heard the names of the other deities.

28. "One of them is Heimdall, called also the White God. He is the son of nine virgins, who were sisters, and is a very sacred and powerful deity. He also bears the appellation of the Gold-toothed, on account of his teeth being of pure gold, and also that of Hallinskithi. His horse is called Gulltopp, and he dwells in Himinbjorg at the end of Bifrost. He is the warder of the gods, and is therefore placed on the borders of heaven, to prevent the giants from forcing their way over the bridge. He requires less sleep than a bird, and sees by night, as well as by day, a hundred miles around him. So acute is his ear that no sound escapes him, for he can even hear the grass growing on the earth, and the wool on a sheep's back. He has a horn called the Gjallar-horn, which is heard throughout the universe. His sword is called Hofud (Head).

HODUR THE BLIND, ASSASSIN OF BALDUR

29. "Among the Æsir," continued Har, "we also reckon Hodur, who is blind, but extremely strong. Both gods and men would be very glad if they never had occasion to pronounce his name, for they will long have cause to remember the deed perpetrated by his hand.[132]

30. "Another god is Vidar, surnamed the Silent, who wears very thick shoes. He is almost as strong as Thor himself, and the gods place great reliance on him in all critical conjunctures.

31. "Vali, another god, is the son of Odin and Rinda, he is bold in war, and an excellent archer.

32. "Another is called Ullur, who is the son of Sif, and stepson of Thor. He is so well skilled in the use of the bow, and can go so fast on his snow-skates, that in these arts

no one can contend with him. He is also very handsome in his person, and possesses every quality of a warrior, wherefore it is befitting to invoke him in single combats.

33. "The name of another god is Forseti, who is the son of Baldur and Nanna, the daughter of Nef. He possesses the heavenly mansion called Glitnir, and all disputants at law who bring their cases before him go away perfectly reconciled.

"His tribunal is the best that is to be found among gods or men.

OF LOKI AND HIS PROGENY.

34. "There is another deity," continued Har, "reckoned in the number of the Æsir, whom some call the calumninator of the gods, the contriver of all fraud and mischief, and the disgrace of gods and men. His name is Loki or Loptur. He is the son of the giant Farbauti. His mother is Laufey or Nal;

his brothers are Byleist and Helblindi. Loki is handsome and well made, but of a very fickle mood, and most evil disposition. He surpasses all beings in those arts called Cunning and Perfidy. Many a time has he exposed the gods to very great perils, and often extricated them again by his artifices. His wife is called Siguna, and their son Nari.

35. "Loki," continued Har, "has likewise had three children by Angurbodi, a giantess of Jotunheim. The first is the wolf Fenrir; the second Jormungand, the Midgard serpent; the third Hela (Death). The gods were not long ignorant that these monsters continued to be bred up in Jotunheim, and, having had recourse to divination, became aware of all the evils they would have to suffer from them; their being sprung from such a mother was a bad presage, and from such a sire was still worse. All-father therefore deemed it advisable to send one of the gods to bring them to him. When they came he threw the serpent into that deep ocean

by which the earth is engirdled. But the monster has grown to such an enormous size that, holding his tail in his mouth, he encircles the whole earth. Hela he cast into Nifelheim, and gave her power over nine worlds (regions), into which she distributes those who are sent to her, that is to say, all who die through sickness or old age. Here she possesses a habitation protected by exceedingly high walls and strongly barred gates. Her hall is called Elvidnir; Hunger is her table; Starvation, her knife; Delay, her man; Slowness, her maid; Precipice, her threshold; Care, her bed; and Burning Anguish forms the hangings of her apartments. The one half of her body is livid, the other half the colour of human flesh. She may therefore easily be recognized; the more so, as she has a dreadfully stern and grim countenance.

"The wolf Fenrir was bred up among the gods; but Tyr alone had the daring to go and feed him. Nevertheless, when the gods perceived that he every day increased prodigiously in size, and that the oracles warned them that he would one day become fatal to them, they determined to make a very strong iron fetter for him, which they called Læding. Taking this fetter to the wolf, they bade him try his strength on it. Fenrir, perceiving that the enterprise would not be very difficult for him, let them do what they pleased, and then, by great muscular exertion, burst the chain and set himself at liberty. The gods, having seen this, made another fetter, half as strong again as the former, which they called Dromi, and prevailed on the wolf to put it on, assuring him that, by breaking this, he would give an undeniable proof of his vigour.

"The wolf saw well enough that it would not be so easy to break this fetter, but finding at the same time that his strength had increased since he broke Læding, and thinking that he could never become famous without running some risk, voluntarily submitted to be chained. When the gods told him that they had finished their task, Fenrir shook himself violently stretched his limbs, rolled on the ground, and at last burst his chains, which flew in pieces all around him. He then freed himself from Dromi, which gave rise to the proverb, 'to get loose out of Læding, or to dash out of Dromi,' when anything is to be accomplished by strong efforts.

BINDING THE WOLF FENIR.

"After this, the gods despaired of ever being able to bind the wolf; wherefore All-father sent Skirnir, the messenger of Frey, into the country of the Dark Elves (Svartalfaheim) to engage certain dwarfs to make the fetter called Gleipnir. It was fashioned out of six things; to wit, the noise made by the footfall of a cat; the beards of women; the roots of stones; the sinews of bears; the breath of fish; and the spittle of birds. Though thou mayest not have heard of these things before, thou mayest easily convince thyself that we have not been telling thee lies. Thou must have seen that women have no beards, that cats make no noise when they run, and that there are no roots under stones. Now I know what has been told thee to be equally true, although there may be some things thou art not able to furnish a proof of."

"I believe what thou hast told me to be true," replied Gangler, "for what thou hast adduced in corroboration of thy statement is conceivable. But how was the fetter smithied?"

"This can I tell thee," replied Har, "that the fetter was as smooth and soft as a silken string, and yet, as thou wilt presently hear, of very great strength. When it was brought to the gods, they were profuse in their thanks to the messenger for the trouble he had given himself; and taking the wolf with them to the island called Lyngvi, in the Lake Amsvartnir, they showed him the cord, and expressed their wish that he would try to break it, assuring him at the same time that it was somewhat stronger than its thinness would warrant a person in supposing it to be. They took it themselves, one after another, in their hands, and after attempting in vain to break it, said, 'Thou alone, Fenrir, art able to accomplish such a feat.'

"'Methinks,' replied the wolf, 'that I shall acquire no fame in breaking such a slender cord; but if any artifice has been employed in making it, slender though it seems, it shall never come on my feet.'

"The gods assured him that he would easily break a limber silken cord, since he had already burst asunder iron fetters of the most solid construction. 'But if thou shouldst not succeed in breaking it,' they added, 'thou wilt show that thou art too weak to cause the gods any fear, and we will not hesitate to set thee at liberty without delay.'

"'I fear me much,' replied he wolf, 'that if ye once bind me so fast that I shall be unable

to free myself by my own efforts, ye will be in no haste to unloose me. Loath am I, therefore, to have this cord wound round me; but in order that ye may not doubt my courage, I will consent, provided one of you put his hand into my mouth as a pledge that ye intend me no deceit.'

"The gods wistfully looked at each other, and found that they had only the choice of two evils, until Tyr stepped forward and intrepidly put his right hand between the monster's jaws. Hereupon the gods, having tied up the wolf, he forcibly stretched himself as he had formerly done, and used all his might to disengage himself, but the more efforts he made the tighter became the cord, until all the gods, except Tyr, who lost his hand, burst into laughter at the sight.

"When the gods saw that the wolf was effectually bound, they took the chain called Gelgja, which was fixed to the fetter, and drew it through the middle of a large rock named

Gjoll, which they sank very deep into the earth; afterwards, to make it still more secure, they fastened the end of the cord to a massive stone called Thviti, which they sank still deeper. The wolf made in vain the most violent efforts to break loose, and opening his tremendous jaws endeavoured to bite them. The gods seeing this, thrust a sword into his mouth, which pierced his under-jaw to the hilt, so that the point touched the palate. He then began to howl horribly, and since that time the foam flows continually from his mouth in such abundance that it forms the river called Von. There will he remain until Ragnarok."

"Verily," said Gangler, "an evil progeny is that of Loki, yet most mighty and powerful; but since the gods have so much to fear from the wolf, why did they not slay him?"

"The gods have so much respect for the sanctity of their peace-steads," replied Har, "that they would not stain them with the blood of the wolf, although prophecy had intimated to them that he must one day become the bane of Odin."

OF THE GODDESSES.

36. "Tell me now," said Gangler, "which are the goddesses?"

"The first," replied Har, "is Frigga, who has a magnificent mansion called Fensalir. The second is Saga, who dwells at Sokkvabekk, a very large and stately abode. The third is Eir, the best of all in the healing art. The fourth, named Gefjon, is a maid, and all those who die maids become her hand-maidens. The fifth is Fulla, who is also a maid, and goes about with her hair flowing over her shoulders, and her head adorned with a gold ribbon. She is entrusted with the toilette and slippers of Frigga, and admitted into the most important secrets of that goddess. Freyja is ranked next to Frigga: she is wedded to a person called Odur, and their daughter, named Hnossa, is so very handsome that whatever is beautiful and precious is called by her name (_hnosir_.) But Odur left his wife in order to travel into very remote countries. Since that time Freyja continually weeps, and her tears are drops of pure gold. She has a great variety of names, for having gone over many countries in search of her husband, each people gave her a different name. She is thus called Mardoll, Horn, Gefn, and Syr, and also Vanadis. She possesses the necklace Brising. The seventh goddess is Sjofna, who delights in turning men's hearts and thoughts to love; hence a wooer is called, from her name, _Sjafni_. The eighth, called Lofna, is so mild and gracious to those who invoke her, that by a peculiar privilege which either All-Father himself or Frigga has given her, she can remove every obstacle that may prevent the union of lovers sincerely attached to each other. Hence her name is applied to denote love, and whatever is beloved by men. Vora, the ninth goddess, listens to the oaths that men take, and particularly to the troth plighted between man and woman, and punishes those who keep not their promises. She is wise and prudent, and so penetrating that nothing remains hidden from her. Syn, the tenth, keeps the door in the hall, and shuts it against those who ought not to enter. She presides at trials when any thing is to be denied on oath, whence the proverb, 'Syn (negation) is set against it,' when ought is denied. Hlina, the eleventh, has the care of those whom Frigga intends to deliver from peril. Snotra, the twelfth, is wise and courteous, and men and women who possess these qualities have her name applied to them. Gna, the thirteenth, is the messenger that Frigga sends into the various worlds on her errands. She has a horse that can run through air and water, called Hofvarpnir. Once, as she drove out, certain Vanir saw her car in the air, when one of them exclaimed,

"'What flieth there? What goeth there?   In the air aloft what glideth?'

She answered,

> "'I fly not though I go,
> And glide through the air
> On Hofvarpnir,   Whose
> sire's Hamskerpir,   And dam
> Gardrofa.'

"Sol and Bil are also reckoned among the goddesses, but their nature has already been explained to thee.

37. "There are besides these a great many other goddesses, whose duty it is to serve in Valhalla; to bear in the drink and take care of the drinking-horns and whatever belongs to the table. They are named in Grimnismal, and are called Valkyrjor. Odin sends them to every field of battle, to make choice of those who are to be slain, and to sway the victory. Gudur, Rota, and the youngest of the Norns, Skuld, also ride forth to choose the slain and turn the combat. Jord (earth), the mother of Thor, and Rinda, the mother of Vali, are also reckoned amongst the goddesses."

OF FREY AND GERDA.

38. "There was a man," continued Har, "named Gymir, who had for wife Aurboda, of the race of the Mountain-giants. Their daughter is Gerda, who is the most beautiful of all women. One day Frey having placed himself in Hlidskjalf, to take a view of the whole universe, perceived, as he looked towards the north, a large and stately mansion which a woman was going to enter, and as she lifted up the latch of the door so great a radiancy was thrown from her hand that the air and waters, and all worlds were illuminated by it. At this sight, Frey, as a just punishment for his audacity in mounting on that sacred throne, was struck with sudden sadness, insomuch so, that on his return home he could neither speak, nor sleep, nor drink, nor did any one dare to inquire the cause of his affliction; but Njord, at last, sent for Skirnir, the messenger of Frey, and charged

him to demand of his master why he thus refused to speak to any one. Skirnir promised to do this, though with great reluctance, fearing that all he had to expect was a severe reprimand. He, however, went to Frey, and asked him boldly why he was so sad and silent. Frey answered, that he had seen a maiden of such surpassing beauty that if he could not possess her he should not live much longer, and that this was what rendered him so melancholy. 'Go, therefore,' he added, 'and ask her hand for me, and bring her here whether her father be willing or not, and I will amply reward thee.' Skirnir undertook to perform the task, provided he might be previously put in possession of Frey's sword, which was of such excellent quality that it would of itself strew a field with carnage whenever the owner ordered it. Frey, impatient of delay, immediately made him a present of the sword, and Skirnir set out on his journey and obtained the maiden's promise, that within nine nights she would come to a place called Barey,

and there wed Frey. Skirnir having reported the success of his message, Frey exclaimed,

"'Long is one night, Long are two nights,   But how shall I hold out three? Shorter hath seemed   A month to me oft   Than of this longing-time the half.'

"Frey having thus given away his sword, found himself without arms when he fought with Beli, and hence it was that he slew him with a stag's antlers."

"But it seems very astonishing," interrupted Gangler, "that such a brave hero as Frey should give away his sword without keeping another equally good for himself. He must have been in a very bad plight when he encountered Beli, and methinks must have mightily repented him of the gift."

"That combat," replied Har, "was a trifling affair. Frey could have killed Beli with a blow of his fist had he felt inclined: but the time will come when the sons of Muspell

37

shall issue forth to the fight, and then, indeed, will Frey truly regret having parted with his falchion."

OF THE JOYS OF

VALHALLA.

39. "If it be as thou hast told me," said Gangler, "that all men who have fallen in fight since the beginning of the world are gone to Odin, in Valhalla, what has he to give them to eat, for methinks there must be a great crowd there?"

"What thou sayest is quite true," replied Har, "the crowd there is indeed great, but great though it be, it will still increase, and will be thought too little when the wolf cometh. But however great the band of men in Valhalla may be, the flesh of the boar Sæhrimnir will more than suffice for their sustenance. For although this boar is sodden every morning he becomes whole again every night. But

there are few, methinks, who are wise enough to give thee, in this respect, a satisfactory answer to thy question. The cook is called Andhrimnir, and the kettle Eldhrimnir. As it is said,--'Andhrimnir cooks in Eldhrimnir, Sæhrimnir.' 'Tis the best of flesh, though few know how much is required for the Einherjar."

"But has Odin," said Gangler, "the same food as the heroes?"

"Odin,' replied Har, 'gives the meat that is set before him to two wolves, called Geri and Freki, for he himself stands in no need of food. Wine is for him both meat and drink.

"Two ravens sit on Odin's shoulders and whisper in his ear the tidings and events they have heard and witnessed. They are called Hugin and Munin.[133] He sends them out at dawn of day to fly over the whole world, and they return at eve towards meal time. Hence it is that Odin knows so many things, and is called the Raven's God. As it is said,--

'Hugin and Munin Each dawn take their flight Earth's fields over.

I fear me for Hugin,   Lest he come not back,   But much more for Munin.'"

40. "What have the heroes to drink," said Gangler, "in sufficient quantity to correspond to their plentiful supply of meat: do they only drink water?"

"A very silly question is that," replied Har; "dost thou imagine that All-Father would invite kings and jarls and other great men and give them nothing to drink but water! In that case, methinks, many of those who had endured the greatest hardships, and received deadly wounds in order to obtain access to Valhalla, would find that they had paid too great a price for their water drink, and would indeed have reason to complain were they there to meet with no better entertainment. But thou wilt see that the case is quite otherwise. For the she-goat, named Heidrun, stands above Valhalla, and feeds on the leaves of a very famous tree called Lærath, and from her teats flows mead in such great abundance that every day a stoop, large enough to hold more than would suffice for all the heroes, is filled with it."

"Verily," said Gangler, "a mighty useful goat is this, and methinks the tree she feeds on must have very singular virtues."

"Still more wonderful," replied Har, "is what is told of the stag Eikthyrnir. This stag also stands over Valhalla and feeds upon the leaves of the same tree, and whilst he is feeding so many drops fall from his antlers down into Hvergelmir that they furnish sufficient water for the rivers that issuing thence flow through the celestial abodes."

41. "Wondrous things are these which thou tellest me of," said Gangler, "and Valhalla must needs be an immense building, but methinks there must often be a great press at the door among such a number of people constantly thronging in and out?"

"Why dost thou not ask," replied Har, "how many doors there are, and what are their dimensions; then wouldst thou be able to judge whether there is any difficulty in going in and out. Know, then, that there is no lack of either seats or doors. As it is said in Grimnismal:--

"'Five hundred doors
And forty more   Methinks
are in Valhalla.   Eight
hundred heroes through
each door   Shall issue forth
Against the wolf to combat.'"

42. "A mighty band of men must be in Valhalla," said Gangler, "and methinks Odin must be a great chieftain to command such a numerous host. But how do the heroes pass their time when they are not drinking?"

"Every day," replied Har, "as soon as they have dressed themselves they ride out into the court (or field), and there fight until they cut each other to pieces. This is their pastime, but when meal-time approaches they remount their steeds and return to drink in Valhalla. As it is said:--

"'The Einherjar all   On
Odin's plain   Hew daily
each other,   While chosen
the slain are.   From the fray
they then ride,   And drink
ale with the Æsir.'

"Thou hast thus reason to say that Odin is great and mighty, for there are many proofs of this. As it is said in the very words of the Æsir:--

"'The ash Yggdrasill   Is
the first of trees,   As Skidbladnir of ships,   Odin of
Æsir,   Sleipnir of steeds,
Bifrost of bridges,   Bragi of
bards,   Habrok of hawks,
And Garm of hounds is.'

OF THE HORSE SLEIPNIR.

43. "Thou mad'st mention," said Gangler, "of the horse Sleipnir. To whom does he belong, and what is there to say respecting him?"

"Thou seemest to know nothing either about Sleipnir or his origin," replied Har, "but thou wilt no doubt find what thou wilt hear worthy of thy notice. Once on a time when the gods were constructing their abodes, and had already finished Midgard and Valhalla, a certain artificer came and offered to build them, in the space of three half years, a residence so well fortified that they should be perfectly safe from the incursion of the Frost-giants, and the giants of the mountains, even although they should have penetrated within Midgard. But he demanded for his reward the goddess Freyja, together with the sun and moon. After long deliberation the Æsir agreed to his terms, provided he would finish the whole work himself without ony one's assistance, and all within the space of one winter, but if anything remained unfinished on the first day of summer, he should forfeit the recompense agreed on. On being told these terms, the artificer stipulated that he should be allowed the use of his horse, called Svadilfari, and this, by the advice of Loki, was granted to him. He accordingly set to work on the first day of winter, and during the night let his horse draw stone for the building. The enormous size of the stones struck the Æsir with astonishment, and they saw clearly that the horse did one half more of the toilsome work than his master. Their bargain, however, had been concluded in the presence of witnesses, and confirmed by solemn oaths, for without these precautions a giant would not have thought himself safe among the Æsir, especially when Thor returned from an expedition he had then undertaken towards the east against evil demons.

"As the winter drew to a close the building was far advanced, and the bulwarks were sufficiently high and massive to render this residence impregnable. In short, when it wanted but three days to summer the only part that remained to be finished was the gateway. Then sat the gods on their seats of justice and entered into consultation, inquiring of one another who among them could have advised to give Freyja away to Jotunheim, or to plunge the heavens in darkness by permitting the giant to carry away the sun and moon. They all agreed that no one but Loki, the son of Laufey, and the author of so many evil deeds, could have given such bad counsel, and that he should be put to a cruel death if he did not contrive some way or other to prevent the artificer from completing his task and obtaining the stipulated recompense. They immediately proceeded to lay hands on Loki, who, in his fright, promised upon oath that let it cost him what it would, he would so manage matters that the man should

lose his reward. That very night, when the artificer went with Svadilfari for building stone, a mare suddenly ran out of a forest and began to neigh. The horse being thus excited, broke loose and ran after the mare into the forest, which obliged the man also to run after his horse, and thus between one and the other the whole night was lost, so that at dawn the work had not made the usual progress. The man seing that he had no other means of completing his task, resumed his own gigantic stature, and the gods now clearly perceived that it was in reality a Mountain-giant who had come amongst them. No longer regarding their oaths, they, therefore, called on Thor, who immediately ran to their assistance, and lifting up his mallet Mjolnir paid the workman his wages, not with the sun and moon, and not even by sending him back to Jotunheim, for with the first blow he shattered the giant's skull to pieces, and hurled him headlong into Nifelhel. But Loki had run such a race with Svadilfari that shortly after he bore a grey foal with

42

eight legs. This is the horse Sleipnir, which excels all horses ever possessed by gods or men."

OF THE SHIP

SKIDBLADNIR.

44. "What hast thou to say," demanded Gangler, "of Skidbladnir, which thou toldst me was the best of ships? Is there no other ship as good or as large?"

"Skidbladnir," replied Har, "is without doubt the best and most artfully constructed of any, but the ship Nagflar is of larger size. They were dwarfs, the sons of Ivaldi, who built Skidbladnir, and made a present of her to Frey. She is so large that all the Æsir with their weapons and war stores find room on board her. As soon as the sails are set a favourable breeze arises and carries her to her place of destination, and she is made of so many pieces, and with so much skill, that when she

is not wanted for a voyage Frey may fold her together like a piece of cloth, and put her in his pocket."

"A good ship truly, is Skidbladnir," said Gangler, "and many cunning contrivances and spells must, no doubt, have been used in her construction."

THOR'S ADVENTURES ON HIS JOURNEY TO THE LAND OF THE GIANTS.

45. "But tell me," he (Gangler) continued, "did it ever happen to Thor in his expeditions to be overcome either by spells or by downright force?"

"Few can take upon them to affirm this," replied Har, "and yet it has often fared hard enough with him; but had he in reality been worsted in any rencounter there would be no need to make mention of it, since all are bound to believe that nothing can resist his power."

"It would, therefore, appear," said Gangler, "that I have asked of you things that none of you are able to tell me of."

"There are, indeed, some such rumours current among us," answered Jafnhar, "but they are hardly credible; however, there is one sitting here can impart them to thee, and thou shouldst the rather believe him, for never having yet uttered an untruth, he will not now begin to deceive thee with false stories."

"Here then will I stand," said Gangler, "and listen to what ye have to say, but if ye cannot answer my question satisfactorily I shall look upon you as vanquished."

Then spake Thridi and said, "We can easily conceive that thou art desirous of knowing these tidings, but it behooves thee to guard a becoming silence respecting them. The story I have to relate is this:--

46. "One day the God Thor set out in his car drawn by two he-goats, and accompanied by Loki, on a journey.

Night coming on, they put up at a peasant's cottage, where Thor killed his goats, and after flaying them, put them in the kettle. When the flesh was sodden, he sat down with his fellow-traveller to supper, and invited the peasant and his family to partake of his repast. The peasant's son was named Thjalfi, and his daughter Roska. Thor bade them throw all the bones into the goats' skins which were spread out near the fire-place, but young Thjalfi broke one of the shank bones with his knife to come to the marrow. Thor having passed the night in the cottage, rose at the dawn of day, and when he was dressed took his mallet Mjolnir, and lifting it up, consecrated the goats' skins, which he had no sooner done than the two goats re-assumed their wonted form, only that one of them now limped on one of its hind legs. Thor perceiving this, said that the peasant, or one of his family, had handled the shank bone of this goat too roughly, for he saw clearly that it was broken. It may readily be imagined how frightened the peasant was when he saw

44

Thor knit his brows, and grasp the handle of his mallet with such force that the joints of his fingers became white from the exertion. Fearing to be struck down by the very looks of the god, the peasant and his family made joint suit for pardon, offering whatever they possessed as an atonement for the offence committed. Thor, seeing their fear, desisted from his wrath, and became more placable, and finally contented himself by requiring the peasant's children, Thjalfi and Roska, who became his bond-servants, and have followed him ever since.

'Leaving his goats with the peasant, Thor proceeded eastward on the road to Jotunheim, until he came to the shores of a vast and deep sea, which having passed over he penetrated into a strange country along with his companions, Loki, Thjalfi, and Roska. They had not gone far before they saw before them an immense forest, through which they wandered all day. Thjalfi was of all men the swiftest of foot. He bore Thor's wallet, but the forest was a bad place for finding anything eatable to stow in it. When it became dark, they searched on all sides for a place where they might pass the night, and at last came to a very large hall with an entrance that took up the whole breadth of one of the ends of the building. Here they chose them a place to sleep in; but towards midnight were alarmed by an earthquake which shook the whole edifice. Thor, rising up, called on his companions to seek with him a place of safety. On the right they found an adjoining chamber, into which they entered, but while the others, trembling with fear, crept into the furthest corner of this retreat, Thor remained at the doorway with his mallet in his hand, prepared to defend himself, whatever might happen. A terrible groaning was heard during the night, and at dawn of day, Thor went out and observed lying near him a man of enormous bulk, who slept and snored pretty loudly. Thor could now account for the noise they had heard over night, and girding on his Belt of Prowess, increased that divine strength which he now stood in need of. The giant awakening, rose up, and it is said that for once in his life Thor was afraid to make use of his mallet, and contented himself by simply asking the giant his name.

"'My name is Skrymir, said the other, 'but I need not ask thy name, for I know thou art the God Thor. But what hast thou done with my glove?' And stretching out his hand Skrymir picked up his glove, which Thor then perceived was what they had taken over night for a hall, the chamber where they had sought refuge being the thumb. Skrymir then asked whether they would have his fellowship, and Thor consenting, the giant opened his wallet and began to eat his breakfast. Thor and his companions having also taken their morning repast, though in another place, Skrymir proposed that they should lay their provisions together, which Thor also assented to. The giant then put all the meat into one wallet, which he slung on his back and went before them, taking tremendous strides, the whole day, and at dusk sought out for them a place where they might pass the night under a large oak tree. Skrymir then told them that he would lie down to sleep. 'But take ye the wallet,' he added, 'and prepare your supper.'

"Skrymir soon fell asleep, and began to snore strongly, but incredible though it may appear, it must nevertheless be told, that when Thor came to open the wallet he could not untie a single knot, nor render a single string looser than it was before. Seeing that his labour was in vain, Thor became wroth, and grasping his mallet with both hands while he advanced a step forward, launched it at the giant's head. Skrymir, awakening, merely asked whether a leaf had not fallen on his head, and whether they had supped and were ready to go to sleep. Thor answered that they were just going to sleep, and so saying, went and laid himself down under another oak tree. But sleep came not that night to

Thor, and when he remarked that Skrymir snored again so loud that the forest re-echoed with the noise, he arose, and grasping his mallet, launched it with such force that it sunk into the giant's skull up to the handle. Skrymir awakening, cried out--

"'What's the matter? did an acorn fall on my head? How fares it with thee, Thor?'

"But Thor went away hastily, saying that he had just then awoke, and that as it was only midnight there was still time for sleep. He however resolved that if he had an opportunity of striking a third blow, it should settle all matters between them. A little before daybreak he perceived that Skrymir was again fast asleep, and again grasping his mallet, dashed it with such violence that it forced its way into the giant's cheek up to the handle. But Skrymir sat up, and stroking his cheek, said--

"'Are there any birds perched on this tree? Methought when I awoke some moss from the branches fell on my head.

What! Art thou awake, Thor? Methinks it is time for us to get up and dress ourselves; but you have not now a long way before you to the city called Utgard. I have heard you whispering to one another that I am not a man of small dimensions; but if you come into Utgard you will see there many men much taller than myself. Wherefore I advise you, when you come there, not to make too much of yourselves, for the followers of Utgard-Loki will not brook the boasting of such manni-kins as ye are. The best thing you could do would probably be to turn back again, but if you persist in going on, take the road that leads eastward, for mine now lies northward to those rocks which you may see in the distance.'

"Hereupon, he threw his wallet over his shoulders and turned away from them, into the forest, and I could never hear that Thor wished to meet with him a second time.

47. "Thor and his compan-ions proceeded on their way, and towards noon descried a

city standing in the middle of a plain. It was so lofty that they were obliged to bend their necks quite back on their shoulders ere they could see to the top of it. On arriving at the walls they found the gateway closed with a gate of bars strongly locked and bolted. Thor, after trying in vain to open it, crept with his companions through the bars, and thus succeeded in gaining admission into the city. Seeing a large palace before them, with the door wide open, they went in and found a number of men of prodigious stature sitting on benches in the hall. Going further, they came before the king, Utgard-Loki, whom they saluted with great respect. Their salutations were however returned by a contemptuous look from the king, who, after regarding them for some time, said with a scornful smile--

"'It is tedious to ask for tidings of a long journey, yet if I do not mistake me, that stripling there must be Aku-Thor. Perhaps,' he added, addressing himself to Thor, 'thou mayst be taller than thou appearest to be. But what are the feats that thou and thy fellows deem yourselves skilled in, for no one is permitted to remain here who does not, in some feat or other, excel all other men.'

"'The feat I know,' replied Loki, 'is to eat quicker than any one else, and in this I am ready to give a proof against any one here who may choose to compete with me.'

"'That will indeed be a feat,' said Utgard-Loki, 'if thou performest what thou promisest, and it shall be tried forthwith.'

"He then ordered one of his men, who was sitting at the further end of the bench, and whose name was Logi,[134] to come forward and try his skill with Loki. A trough filled with flesh meat having been set on the hall floor, Loki placed himself at one end, and Logi at the other, and each of them, began to eat as fast as he could, until they met in the middle of the trough. But it was found that Loki had only eaten the flesh, whereas his adversary had devoured both flesh and bone, and the trough to boot. All the company therefore adjudged that Loki was vanquished.

"Utgard-Loki then asked what feat the young man who accompanied Thor could perform. Thjalfi answered that he would run a race with any one who might be matched against him. The king observed that skill in running was something to boast of, but that if the youth would win the match he must display great agility. He then arose and went with all who were present to a plain where there was a good ground for running on, and calling a young man named Hugi,[135] bade him run a match with Thjalfi. In the first course Hugi so much outstripped his competitor that he turned back and met him not far from the starting-place.

"'Thou must ply thy legs better, Thjalfi,' said Utgard-Loki, 'if thou wilt win the match, though I must needs say that there never came a man here swifter of foot than thou art.'

"In the second course, Thjalfi was a full bow-shot from the goal when Hugi arrived at it.

"'Most bravely dost thou run, Thjalfi,' said Utgard-Loki, 'though thou wilt not, methinks, win the match. But the third, course must decide.'

"They accordingly ran a third time, but Hugi had already reached the goal before Thjalfi had got half way. All who were present then cried out that there had been a sufficient trial of skill in this kind of exercise.

50. "Utgard-Loki then asked Thor in what feats he would choose to give proofs of that dexterity for which he was so famous. Thor replied, that he would begin a drinking match with any one. Utgard-Loki consented, and entering the palace, bade his cupbearer bring the large horn which his followers were obliged to drink out of when they had trespassed in any way against established usage. The cup-

49

bearer having presented it to Thor, Utgard-Loki said--

"'Whoever is a good drinker will empty that horn at a single draught, though some men make two of it, but the most puny drinker of all can do it at three.'

"Thor looked at the horn, which seemed of no extraordinary size, though somewhat long; however, as he was very thirsty, he set it to his lips, and without drawing breath pulled as long and as deeply as he could, that he might not be obliged to make a second draught of it; but when he set the horn down and looked in, he could scarcely perceive that the liquor was diminished.

"''Tis well drunken,' exclaimed Utgard-Loki, 'though nothing much to boast of; and I would not have believed had it been told me that Asa-Thor could not have taken a greater draught, but thou no doubt meanest to make amends at the second pull.'

"Thor, without answering, went to it again with all his might, but when he took the horn from his mouth it seemed to him as if he had drunk rather less than before, although the horn could now be carried without spilling.

"'How now, Thor,' said Utgard-Loki; 'thou must not spare thyself more in performing a feat than befits thy skill; but if thou meanest to drain the horn at the third draught thou must pull deeply; and I must needs say that thou wilt not be called so mighty a man here as thou art among the Æsir, if thou showest no greater prowess in other feats than, methinks, will be shown in this.'

"Thor, full of wrath, again set the horn to his lips, and exerted himself to the utmost to empty it entirely, but on looking in found that the liquor was only a little lower, upon which he resolved to make no further attempt, but gave back the horn to the cupbearer.

51. "'I now see plainly,' said Utgard-Loki, 'that thou are not quite so stout as we thought thee, but wilt thou try any other feat, though, methinks, thou art not likely to bear any prize away with thee hence.'

"'I will try another feat,' replied Thor, 'and I am sure such draughts as I have been drinking would not have been reckoned small among the Æsir; but what new trial hast thou to propose?'

"'We have a very, trifling game here,' answered Ut-gard-Loki, 'in which we exercise none but children. It consists in merely lifting my cat from the ground, nor should I have dared to mention such a feat to Asa-Thor if I had not already observed that thou art by no means what we took thee for.'

"As he finished speaking, a large grey cat sprung on the hall floor. Thor advancing put his hand under the cat's belly, and did his utmost to raise him from the floor, but the cat bending his back had, notwithstanding all Thor's efforts, only one of his feet lifted up, seeing which, Thor made no further attempt.

"'This trial has turned out,' said Utgard-Loki, 'just as I imagined it would; the cat is large, but Thor is little in comparison to our men.'

"'Little as ye call me,' answered Thor, 'let me see who amongst you will come hither now I am in wrath, and wrestle with me.'

"'I see no one here,' said Utgard-Loki, looking at the men sitting on the benches, 'who would not think it beneath him to wrestle with thee; let somebody, however, call hither that old crone, my nurse Elli,[136] and let Thor wrestle with her if he will. She has thrown to the ground many a man not less strong and mighty than this Thor is.'

53. "A toothless old woman then entered the hall, and was told by Utgard-Loki to take hold of Thor. The tale is

51

shortly told. The more Thor tightened his hold on the crone the firmer she stood. At length, after a very violent struggle, Thor began to lose his footing, and was finally brought down upon one knee. Utgard-Loki then told them to desist, adding that Thor had now no occasion to ask any one else in the hall to wrestle with him, and it was also getting late. He therefore showed Thor and his companions to their seats, and they passed the night there in good cheer.

54. "The next morning, at break of day, Thor and his companions dressed themselves and prepared for their departure. Utgard-Loki then came and ordered a table to be set for them, on which there was no lack either of victuals or drink. After the repast Utgard-Loki led them to the gate of the city, and, on parting, asked Thor how he thought his journey had turned out, and whether he had met with any men stronger than himself. Thor told him that he could not deny but that he had brought great

shame on himself. 'And what grieves me most,' he added, 'is that ye will call me a man of little worth.'

55. "'Nay,' said Utgard-Loki, 'it behooves me to tell thee the truth now thou are out of the city which so long as I live, and have my way, thou shalt never re-enter. And by my troth, had I known beforehand that thou hadst so much strength in thee, and wouldst have brought me so near to a great mishap, I would not have suffered thee to enter this time. Know then that I have all along deceived thee by my illusions; first, in the forest, where I arrived before thee, and there thou wert not able to untie the wallet, because I had bound it with iron wire, in such a manner that thou couldst not discover how the knot ought to be loosened. After this, thou gavest me three blows with thy mallet; the first, though the least, would have ended my days had it fallen on me, but I brought a rocky mountain before me which thou didst not perceive, and in this mountain thou wilt

find three glens, one of them remarkably deep. These are the dints made by thy mallet. I have made use of similar illusions in the contests ye have had with my followers. In the first, Loki, like hunger itself, devoured all that was set before him, but Logi was, in reality, nothing else than ardent fire, and therefore consumed not only the meat but the trough which held it. Hugi, with whom Thjalfi contended in running, was Thought, and it was impossible for Thjalfi to keep pace with that. When thou, in thy turn, didst try to empty the horn, thou didst perform, by my troth, a deed so marvellous, that had I not seen it myself I should never have believed it. For one end of that horn reached the sea, which thou wast not aware of, but when thou comest to the shore thou wilt perceive how much the sea has sunk by thy draughts, which have caused what is now called the ebb. Thou didst perform a feat no less wonderful by lifting up the cat, and to tell thee the truth, when we saw that one of his paws was off the floor, we were all of us terror-stricken, for what thou tookest for a cat was in reality the great Midgard serpent that encompassed the whole earth, and he was then barely long enough to inclose it between his head and tail, so high had thy hand raised him up towards heaven. Thy wrestling with Elli was also a most astonishing feat, for there was never yet a man, nor ever shall be, whom Old Age, for such in fact was Elli, will not sooner or later lay low if he abide her coming. But now as we are going to part, let me tell thee that it will be better for both of us if thou never come near me again, for shouldst thou do so, I shall again defend myself by other illusions, so that thou wilt never prevail against me.'

"On hearing these words, Thor, in a rage, laid hold of his mallet and would have launched it at him, but Utgard-Loki had disappeared, and when Thor would have returned to the city to-destroy it, he found nothing around him but a verdant plain. Proceeding, therefore, on his way, he returned without stopping to Thrudvang. But he had already resolved to make that attack on the Midgard serpent which afterwards took place. I trust," concluded Thridi, "that thou wilt now acknowledge that no one can tell thee truer tidings than those thou hast heard respecting this journey of Thor to Jotunheim."

HOW THOR WENT TO FISH FOR THE MID-GARD SERPENT.

56. "I find by your account," said Gangler, "that Utgard-Loki possesses great might in himself, though he has recourse to spells and illusions; but his power may be seen by his followers, being in every respect so skillful and dexterous. But tell me, did Thor ever avenge this affront?"

"It is not unknown," replied Har, "though nobody has talked of it, that Thor was determined to make amends for the journey just spoken of, and he had not been long at home ere he set out again

so hastily that he had neither his car nor his goats, nor any followers with him. He went out of Midgard under the semblance of a young man, and came at dusk to the dwelling of a giant called Hymir. Here Thor passed the night, but at break of day, when he perceived that Hymir was making his boat ready for fishing, he arose and dressed himself, and begged the giant would let him row out to sea with him. Hymir answered, that a puny stripling like he was could be of no great use to him. 'Besides,' he added, 'thou wilt catch thy death of cold if I go so far out and remain so long as I am accustomed to do.' Thor said, that for all that, he would row as far from the land as Hymir had a mind, and was not sure which of them would be the first who might wish to row back again. At the same time he was so enraged that he felt sorely inclined to let his mallet ring on the giant's skull without further delay, but intending to try his strength elsewhere, he stifled his wrath, and asked Hymir what he meant to bait

54

with. Hymir told him to look out for a bait himself. Thor instantly went up to a herd of oxen that belonged to the giant, and seizing the largest bull, that bore the name of Himinbrjot, wrung off his head, and returning with it to the boat, put out to sea with Hymir. Thor rowed aft with two oars, and with such force that Hymir, who rowed at the prow, saw with surprise, how swiftly the boat was driven forward. He then observed that they were come to the place where he was wont to angle for flat fish, but Thor assured him that they had better go on a good way further. They accordingly continued to ply their oars, until Hymir cried out that if they did not stop they would be in danger from the great Midgard serpent. Notwith-standing this, Thor persisted in rowing further, and in spite of Hymir's remonstrances was a great while before he would lay down his oars. He then took out a fishing-line, ex-tremely strong, furnished with an equally strong hook, on which he fixed the bull's head, and cast his line into the sea.

The bait soon reached the bottom, and it may be truly said that Thor then deceived the Midgard serpent not a whit less than Utgard-Loki had deceived Thor when he obliged him to lift up the serpent in his hand: for the monster greedily caught at the bait, and the hook stuck fast in his palate. Stung with the pain, the serpent tugged at the hook so violently, that Thor was obliged to hold fast with both hands by the pegs that bear against the oars. But his wrath now waxed high, and assuming all his divine power, he pulled so hard at the line that his feet forced their way through the boat and went down to the bottom of the sea, whilst with his hands he drew up the serpent to the side of the vessel. It is impossible to express by words the dreadful scene that now took place. Thor, on one hand, darting looks of ire on the serpent, whilst the monster, rearing his head, spouted out floods of venom upon him. It is said that when the giant Hymir beheld the serpent, he turned pale and trembled with fright and seeing, moreover, that the water was entering his boat on all sides, he took out his knife, just as Thor raised his mallet aloft, and cut the line, on which the serpent sunk again under the water. Thor, however, launched his mallet at him, and there are some who say that it struck off the monster's head at the bottom of the sea, but one may assert with more certainty that he still lives and lies in the ocean. Thor then struck Hymir such a blow with his fist, nigh the ear, that the giant fell headlong into the water, and Thor, wading with rapid strides, soon came to the land again."

THE DEATH OF BALDUR THE GOOD.

57. "Verily," said Gangler, "it was a famous exploit which Thor performed on that journey, but did any other such events take place among the Æsir?"

"Ay," replied Har, "I can tell thee of another event which the Æsir deemed of much greater importance. Thou must know, therefore, that Baldur the Good having been tormented with terrible dreams, indicating that his life was in great peril, communicated them to the assembled Æsir, who resolved to conjure all things to avert from him the threatened danger. Then Frigga exacted an oath from fire and water, from iron, and all other metals, as well as from stones, earths, diseases, beasts, birds, poisons, and creeping things, that none of them would do any harm to Baldur. When this was done, it became a favourite pastime of the Æsir, at their meetings, to get Baldur to stand up and serve them as a mark, some hurling darts at him, some stones, while others hewed at him with their swords and battle-axes, for do they what they would none of therm could harm him, and this was regarded by all as a great honour shown to Baldur. But when Loki, the son of Laufey, beheld the scene, he was sorely vexed that Baldur was not hurt. Assuming, therefore, the shape of a woman, he went to Fensalir, the mansion of Frigga. That goddess, when she saw the pretended woman, inquired of her if she knew what the Æsir were doing at their meetings. She replied, that they were throwing darts and stones at Baldur without being able to hurt him.

"'Ay,' said Frigga, 'neither metal nor wood can hurt Baldur, for I have exacted an oath from all of them.'

"'What!' exclaimed the woman, 'have all things sworn to spare Baldur?'

"'All things,' replied Frigga, 'except one little shrub that grows on the eastern side of Valhalla, and is called Mistletoe, and which I thought too young and feeble to crave an oath from.'

"As soon as Loki heard this he went away, and, resuming his natural shape, cut off the mistletoe, and repaired to the place where the gods were assembled. There he found Hodur standing apart, without partaking of the sports, on account of his blindness, and going up to him, said,

'Why dost thou not also throw something at Baldur?'

"'Because I am blind,' answered Hodur, 'and see not where Baldur is, and have, moreover, nothing to throw with.'

"'Come then,' said Loki, 'do like the rest, and show honour to Baldur by throwing this twig at him, and I will direct thy arm, toward the place where he stands.'

58. "Hodur then took the mistletoe, and under the guidance of Loki, darted it at Baldur, who, pierced through and through, fell down lifeless. Surely never was there witnessed, either among gods or men, a more atrocious deed than this! When Baldur fell the Æsir were struck speechless with horror, and then they looked at each other, and all were of one mind to lay hands on him who had done the deed, but they were obliged to delay their vengeance out of respect for the sacred place (Peacestead) where they were assembled. They at length gave

vent to their grief by loud lamentations, though not one of them could find words to express the poignancy of his feelings. Odin, especially, was more sensible than the others of the loss they had suffered, for he foresaw what a detriment Baldur's death would be to the Æsir. When the gods came to themselves, Frigga asked who among them wished to gain all her love and good will; 'For this,' said she, 'shall he have who will ride to Hel and try to find Baldur, and offer Hela a ransom if she will let him return to Asgard;' whereupon Hermod, surnamed the Nimble, the son of Odin, offered to undertake the journey. Odin's horse Sleipnir was then led forth, on which Hermod mounted, and galloped away on his mission.

59. "The Æsir then took the dead body and bore it to the seashore, where stood Baldur's ship Hringhorn, which passed for the largest in the world. But when they wanted to launch it in order to make Baldur's funeral pile on it, they were unable to make it stir. In this conjuncture they sent to Jotunheim for a certain giantess named Hyrrokin, who came mounted on a wolf, having twisted serpents for a bridle. As soon as she alighted, Odin ordered four Berserkir to hold her steed fast, who were, however, obliged to throw the animal on the ground ere they could effect their purpose. Hyrrokin then went to the ship, and with a single push set it afloat, but the motion was so violent that the fire sparkled from the rollers, and the earth shook all around. Thor, enraged at the sight, grasped his mallet, and but for the interference of the Æsir would have broken the woman's skull. Baldur's body was then borne to the funeral pile on board the ship, and this ceremony had such an effect on Nanna, the daughter of Nep, that her heart broke with grief, and her body was burnt on the same pile with her husband's. Thor then stood up and hallowed the pile with Mjolnir, and during the ceremony kicked a dwarf named Litur, who was running before his feet, into the fire. There was

a vast concourse of various kinds of people at Baldur's obsequies. First came Odin, accompanied by Frigga, the Valkyrjor and his ravens; then Frey in his car drawn by a boar named Gullinbursti or Slidrugtanni; Heimdall rode his horse called Gulltopp, and Freyja drove in her chariot drawn by cats. There were also a great many Frost-giants and giants of the mountains present. Odin laid on the pile the gold ring called Draupnir, which afterwards acquired the property of producing every ninth night eight rings of equal weight. Baldur's horse was led to the pile fully caparisoned, and consumed in the same flames on the body of his master.

BALDUR IN THE ABODE OF THE DEAD.

60. "Meanwhile, Hermod was proceeding on his mission. For the space of nine days, and as many nights, he rode through deep glens so dark that he could not discern anything until he arrived at the river Gjoll, which he passed over on a bridge covered with glittering gold. Modgudur, the maiden who kept the bridge, asked him his name and lineage, telling him that the day before five bands of dead persons had ridden over the bridge, and did not shake it so much as he alone. 'But,' she added, 'thou hast not death's hue on thee, why then ridest them here on the way to Hel?'

"'I ride to Hel,' answered Hermod, 'to seek Baldur. Hast thou perchance seen him pass this way?'

"'Baldur,' she replied, 'hath ridden over Gjoll's bridge, but there below, towards the north, lies the way to the abodes of death.'

"Hermod then pursued his journey until he came to the barred gates of Hel. Here he alighted, girthed his saddle tighter, and remounting, clapped both spurs to his horse, who cleared the gate by a tremendous leap without touching it. Hermod then rode on to the palace, where he found his brother Baldur occupying the most distinguished seat in the hall, and passed the night in his company. The next morning he besought Hela (Death) to let Baldur ride home with him, assuring her that nothing but lamentations were to be heard among the gods. Hela answered that it should now be tried whether Baldur was so beloved as he was said to be.

"'If therefore,' she added, 'all things in the world, both living and lifeless, weep for him, then shall he return to the Æsir, but if any one thing speak against him or refuse to weep, he shall be kept in Hel.'

"Hermod then rose, and Baldur led him out of the hall and gave him the ring Draupnir, to present as a keepsake to Odin. Nanna also sent Frigga a linen cassock and other gifts, and to Fulla a gold finger-ring. Hermod then rode back to Asgard, and gave an account of all he had heard and witnessed.

"The gods upon this dispatched messengers through-out the world, to beg everything to weep, in order that Baldur might be delivered from Hel. All things very willingly complied with this request, both men and every other living being, as well as earths and stones, and trees and metals, just as thou must have seen these things weep when they are brought from a cold place into a hot one. As the messengers were returning with the conviction that their mission had been quite successful, they found an old hag named Thaukt sitting in a cavern, and begged her to weep Baldur out of Hel.

"It was strongly suspected that this hag was no other than Loki himself who never ceased to work evil among the Æsir."

THE FLIGHT AND PUN-
ISHMENT OF LOKI.

61. "Evil are the deeds of Loki truly," said Gangler; "first of all in his having caused Baldur to be slain, and then preventing him from being delivered out of Hel. But was he not punished for these crimes?"

"Ay," replied Har, "and in such a manner that he will long repent having committed them. When he perceived how exasperated the gods were, he fled and hid himself in the mountains. There he built him a dwelling with four doors, so that he could see everything that passed around him. Often in the daytime he assumed the likeness of a salmon, and concealed himself under the waters of a cascade called Franangursfors, where he employed himself in divining and circumventing whatever stratagems the Æsir might have recourse to in order to catch him. One day, as he sat in his dwelling, he took flax and yarn, and worked

them into meshes in the manner that nets have since been made by fishermen. Odin, however, had descried his retreat out of Hlidskjalf, and Loki becoming aware that the gods were approaching, threw his net into the fire, and ran to conceal himself in the river. When the gods entered the house, Kvasir, who was the most distinguished among them all for his quickness and penetration, traced out in the hot embers the vestiges of the net which had been burnt, and told Odin that it must be an invention to catch fish. Whereupon they set to work and wove a net after the model they saw imprinted in the ashes. This net, when finished, they threw into the river in which Loki had hidden himself. Thor held one end of the net, and all the other gods laid hold of the other end, thus jointly drawing it along the stream. Notwithstanding all their precautions the net passed over Loki, who had crept between two stones, and the gods only perceived that some living thing had touched the meshes. They therefore cast their net a second time, hanging so great a weight to it that it everywhere raked the bed of the river. But Loki, perceiving that he had but a short distance from the sea, swam onwards and leapt over the net into the waterfall. The Æsir instantly followed him, and divided themselves into two bands. Thor, wading along in mid-stream, followed the net, whilst the others dragged it along towards the sea. Loki then perceived that he had only two chances of escape, either to swim out to sea, or to leap again over the net. He chose the latter, but as he took a tremendous leap Thor caught him in his hand. Being, however, extremely slippery, he would have escaped had not Thor held him fast by the tail, and this is the reason why salmons have had their tails ever since so fine and thin.

"The gods having thus captured Loki, dragged him without commiseration into a cavern, wherein they placed three sharp-pointed rocks, boring a hole through each of them. Having also seized Loki's children, Vali and Nari, they changed the former into a wolf, and in this likeness he tore his brother to pieces and devoured him. The gods then made cords of his intestines, with which they bound Loki on the points of the rocks, one cord passing under his shoulders, another under his loins, and a third under his hams, and afterwards transformed these cords into thongs of iron. Skadi then suspended a serpent over him in such a manner that the venom should fall on his face, drop by drop. But Siguna, his wife, stands by him and receives the drops as they fall in a cup, which she empties as often as it is filled. But while she is doing this, venom falls upon Loki, which makes him howl with horror, and twist his body about so violently that the whole earth shakes, and this produces what men call earthquakes. There will Loki lie until Ragnarok."

OF RAGNAROK, OR THE TWILIGHT OE THE GODS, AND THE CONFLAGRATION OF THE UNIVERSE.

63. "I have not heard before of Ragnarok," said Gangler; "what hast thou to tell me about it?"

"There are many very notable circumstances concerning it," replied Har, "which I can inform thee of. In the first place will come the winter, called Fimbul-winter, during which snow will fall from the four corners of the world; the frosts will be very severe, the wind piercing, the weather tempestuous, and the sun impart no gladness. Three such winters shall pass away without being tempered by a single summer. Three other similar winters follow, during which war and discord will spread over the whole globe. Brethren for the sake of mere gain shall kill each other, and no one shall spare either his parents or his children.

64. "Then shall happen such things as may truly be accounted great prodigies. The wolf shall devour the sun, and a severe loss will that be for mankind. The other wolf will take the moon, and this too will cause great mischief. Then the stars shall be hurled from the heavens, and the earth so violently shaken that trees will be torn up by the roots, the tottering mountains tumble headlong from their foundations, and all bonds and fetters be shivered in pieces. Fenrir then breaks loose, and the sea rushes over the earth, on account of the Midgard serpent turning with giant force, and gaining the land. On the waters floats the ship Naglfar, which is constructed of the nails of dead men. For which reason great care should be taken to die with pared nails, for he who dies with his nails unpared, supplies materials for the building of this vessel, which both gods and men wish may be finished as late as possible. But in this flood shall Naglfar float, and the giant Hrym be its steersman.

"The wolf Fenrir advancing, opens his enormous mouth; the lower jaw reaches to the earth, and the upper one to heaven, and would in fact reach still farther were there space to admit of it. Fire flashes from his eyes and nostrils. The Midgard serpent, placing himself by the side of the wolf, vomits forth floods of poison which overwhelm the air and the waters. Amidst this devastation heaven is cleft in twain, and the sons of Muspell ride through the breach. Surtur rides first, and both before and behind him flames burning fire. His sword outshines the sun itself. Bifrost, as they ride over it, breaks to pieces. Then they direct their course to the battlefield called Vigrid. Thither also repair the wolf Fenrir and the Midgard serpent, and also Loki, with all the followers of Hel, and Hrym with all the Hrimthursar. But the sons of Muspell keep their effulgent bands apart on the field of battle, which is one hundred miles long on every side.

65. "Meanwhile Heimdall stands up, and with all his force sounds the Gjallar-horn to arouse the gods, who assemble without delay. Odin then rides to Mimir's well and consults Mimir how he and his warriors ought to enter into action. The ash Yggdrasill begins to shake, nor is there anything in heaven or earth exempt from fear at that terrible hour. The Æsir and all the heroes of Valhalla arm themselves and speed forth to the field, led on by Odin, with his golden helm and resplendent cuirass, and his spear called Gungnir. Odin places himself against the wolf Fenrir; Thor stands by his side, but can render him no assistance, having himself to combat with the Midgard serpent. Frey encounters Surtur, and terrible blows are exchanged ere Frey falls; and he owes his defeat to his not having that trusty sword he gave to Skirnir. That day the dog Garm, who had been chained in the Gnipa cave, breaks loose. He is the most fearful monster of all, and attacks Tyr, and they kill each other. Thor gains great renown for killing the

Midgard serpent, but at the same time, recoiling nine paces, falls dead upon the spot suffocated by the floods of venom which the dying serpent vomits forth upon him. The wolf swallows Odin, but at that instant Vidar advances, and setting his foot on the monster's lower jaw, seizes the other with his hand, and thus tears and rends him till he dies. Vidar is able to do this because he wears those shoes for which stuff has been gathering in all ages, namely, the shreds of leather which are cut off to form the toes and heels of shoes, and it is on this account that those who would render a service to the Æsir should take care to throw such shreds away. Loki and Heimdall fight, and mutually kill each other.

"After this, Surtur darts fire and flame over the earth, and the whole universe is consumed."

OF THE ABODES OF FUTURE BLISS AND MISERY.

66. "What will remain," said Gangler, "after heaven and earth and the whole universe shall be consumed, and after all the gods, and the heroes of Valhalla, and all mankind shall have perished? For ye have already told me that every one shall continue to exist in some world or other, throughout eternity."

"There will be many abodes," replied Thridi, "some good, others bad. The best place of all to be in will be Gimli, in heaven, and all who delight in quaffing good drink will find a great store in the hall called Brimir, which is also in heaven in the region Okolni. There is also a fair hall of ruddy gold called Sindri, which stands on the mountains of Nida, (Nidafjoll). In those halls righteous and well-minded men shall abide. In Nastrond there is a vast and direful structure with doors that face the north. It is formed entirely of the backs of serpents, wattled together like wicker work. But the serpents' heads are turned towards the inside of the hall, and continually vomit forth floods of venom, in which wade all those who commit murder, or who forswear themselves."

THE RENOVATION OF THE UNIVERSE.

67. "Will any of the gods survive, and will there be any longer a heaven and an earth?" demanded Gangler.

"There will arise out of the sea," replied Har, "another earth most lovely and verdant, with pleasant fields where the grain shall grow unsown. Vidar and Vali shall survive; neither the flood nor Surtur's fire shall harm them. They shall dwell on the plain of Ida, where Asgard formerly stood. Thither shall come the sons of Thor, Modi and Magni, bringing with them their father's mallet Mjolnir. Baldur and Hodur shall also

repair thither from the abode of death (Hel). There shall they sit and converse together, and call to mind their former knowledge and the perils they underwent, and the fight of the wolf Fenrir and the Midgard serpent. There too shall they find in the grass those golden tablets (orbs) which the Æsir once possessed. As it is said,--

"'There dwell Vidar and Vali   In the gods' holy seats, When slaked Surtur's fire is   But Modi and Magni   Will Mjolnir possess,   And strife put an end to.'

"Thou must know, moreover, that during the conflagration caused by Surtur's fire, a woman named Lif (Life), and a man named Lifthrasir, lie concealed in Hodmimir's forest. They shall feed on morning dew, and their descendants shall soon spread over the whole earth.

"But what thou wilt deem more wonderful is, that the sun shall have brought forth a daughter more lovely than herself, who shall go in the same track formerly trodden by her mother.

"And now," continued Thridi, "if thou hast any further questions to ask, I know not who can answer thee, for I never heard tell of any one who could relate what will happen in the other ages of the world. Make, therefore, the best use thou canst of what has been imparted to thee."

Upon this Gangler heard a terrible noise all around him: he looked everywhere, but could see neither palace nor city, nor anything save a vast plain. He therefore set out on his return to his own kingdom, where he related all that he had seen and heard, and ever since that time these tidings have been handed down by oral tradition.

BRAGI'S TALK

ÆGIR'S JOURNEY TO ASGARD.

68. Ægir, who was well skilled in magic, once went to Asgard, where he met with a very good reception. Supper time being come, the twelve mighty Æsir,--Odin, Thor, Njord, Frey, Tyr, Heimdall, Bragi, Vidar, Vali, Ullur, Hoenir and Forseti, together with the Asynjor,--Frigga, Freyja, Gefjon, Iduna, Gerda, Siguna, Fulla and Nanna, seated themselves on their lofty doom seats, in a hall around which were ranged swords of such surpassing brilliancy that no other light was requisite. They continued long at table, drinking mead of a very superior quality. While they were emptying their capacious drinking horns, Ægir, who sat next to Bragi, requested him to relate something concerning the Æsir. Bragi instantly complied with his request, by informing him of what had happened to Iduna.

IDUNA AND HER APPLES.

69. "Once," he said, "when Odin, Loki, and Hoenir went on a journey, they came to a valley where a herd of oxen were grazing, and being sadly in want of provisions did not scruple to kill one for their supper. Vain, however, were their efforts to boil the flesh; they found it, every time they took off the lid of the kettle, as raw as when first put in. While they were endeavouring to account for this singular circumstance a noise was heard above them, and on looking up they beheld an enormous eagle perched on the branch of an oak tree. 'If ye are willing to let me have my share of the flesh,' said the eagle, 'it shall soon be boiled;' and on their assenting to this proposal, it flew down and snatched up a leg and two shoulders of the ox--a proceeding which so incensed Loki, that he laid hold of a

large stock, and made it fall pretty heavily on the eagle's back. It was, however, not an eagle that Loki struck, but the renowned giant Thjassi, clad in his eagle plumage. Loki soon found this out to his cost, for while one end of the stock stuck fast to the eagle's back, he was unable to let go his hold of the other end, and was consequently trailed by the eagle-clad giant over rocks and forests, until he was almost torn to pieces. Loki in this predicament began to sue for peace, but Thjassi told him that he should never be released from his hold until he bound himself by a solemn oath to bring Iduna and her apples out of Asgard. Loki very willingly gave his oath to effect this object, and went back in a piteous plight to his companions.

70. "On his return to Asgard, Loki told Iduna that, in a forest at a short distance from the celestial residence, he had found apples growing which he thought were of a much better quality than her own, and that at all events it was worth while making a comparison between them. Iduna, deceived by his words, took her apples, and went with him into the forest, but they had no sooner entered it than Thjassi, clad in his eagle-plumage, flew rapidly towards them, and catching up Iduna, carried her treasure off with him to Jotunheim. The gods being thus deprived of their renovating apples, soon became wrinkled and grey; old age was creeping fast upon them, when they discovered that Loki had been, as usual, the contriver of all the mischief that had befallen them. They therefore threatened him with condign punishment if he did not instantly hit upon some expedient for bringing back Iduna and her apples to Asgard. Loki having borrowed from Freyja her falcon-plumage, flew to Jotunheim, and finding that Thjassi was out at sea fishing, lost no time in changing Iduna into a sparrow and flying off with her; but when Thjassi returned and became aware of what had happened, he donned his eagle-plumage, and flew after them. When the Æsir saw Loki

approaching, holding Iduna transformed into a sparrow between his claws, and Thjassi with his outspread eagle wings ready to overtake him, they placed on the walls of Asgard bundles of chips, which they set fire to the instant that Loki had flown over them; and as Thjassi could not stop his flight, the fire caught his plumage, and he thus fell into the power of the Æsir, who slew him within the portals of the celestial residence. When these tidings came to Thjassi's daughter, Skadi, she put on her armour and went to Asgard, fully determined to avenge her father's death; but the Æsir having declared their willingness to atone for the deed, an amicable arrangement was entered into. Skadi was to choose a husband in Asgard, and the Æsir were to make her laugh, a feat which she flattered herself it would be impossible for any one to accomplish. Her choice of a husband was to be determined by a mere inspection of the feet of the gods, it being stipulated that the feet should be the only part of their persons visible until she had made known her determination. In inspecting the row of feet placed before her, Skadi took a fancy to a pair which she flattered herself, from their fine proportions, must be those of Baldur. They were however Njord's, and Njord was accordingly given her for a husband, and as Loki managed to make her laugh, by playing some diverting antics with a goat, the atonement was fully effected. It is even said that Odin did more than had been stipulated, by taking out Thjassi's eyes, and placing them to shine as stars in the firmament.[137]

THE ORIGIN OF

POETRY.

71. Ægir having expressed a wish to know how poetry originated, Bragi informed him that the Æsir and Vanir having met to put an end to the war which had long been carried on between them, a treaty of peace was agreed to and ratified by each party spitting into a jar. As

a lasting sign of the amity which was thenceforward to subsist between the contending parties, the gods formed out of this spittle a being to whom they gave the name of Kvasir, and whom they endowed with such a high degree of intelligence that no one could ask him a question that he was unable to answer. Kvasir then traversed the whole world to teach men wisdom, but was at length treacherously murdered by the dwarfs, Fjalar and Galar, who, by mixing up his blood with honey, composed a liquor of such surpassing excellence that whoever drinks of it acquires the gift of song. When the Æsir inquired what had become of Kvasir, the dwarfs told them that he had been suffocated with his own wisdom, not being able to find any one who by proposing to him a sufficient number of learned questions might relieve him of its superabundance. Not long after this event, Fjalar and Galar managed to drown the giant Gilling and murder his wife, deeds which were avenged by their son Suttung taking the dwarfs out to sea, and placing them on a shoal which was flooded at high water. In this critical position they implored Suttung to spare their lives, and accept the verse-inspiring beverage which they possessed as an atonement for their having killed his parents. Suttung having agreed to these conditions, released the dwarfs, and carrying the mead home with him, committed it to the care of his daughter Gunnlauth. Hence poetry is indifferently called Kvasir's blood, Suttung's mead, the dwarf's ransom, etc.

ODIN BEGUILES THE DAUGHTER OF BAUGI

72. Æsir then asked how the gods obtained possession of so valuable a beverage, on which Bragi informed him that Odin being fully determined to acquire it, set out for Jotunheim, and after journeying for some time, came to a meadow in which nine thralls were mowing. Entering into conversation with

them, Odin, offered to whet their scythes, an offer which they gladly accepted, and finding that the whetstone he made use of had given the scythes an extraordinary sharpness, asked him whether he was willing to dispose of it. Odin, however, threw the whetstone in the air, and in attempting to catch it as it fell, each thrall brought his scythe to bear on the neck of one of his comrades, so that they were all killed in the scramble. Odin took up his night's lodging at the house of Suttung's brother, Baugi, who told him that he was sadly at a loss for labourers, his nine thralls having slain each other. Odin, who went under the name of Baulverk, said that for a draught of Suttung's mead he would do the work of nine men for him. The terms agreed on, Odin worked for Baugi the whole summer, but Suttung was deaf to his brother's entreaties, and would not part with a drop of the precious liquor, which was carefully preserved in a cavern under his daughter's custody. Into this cavern Odin was resolved to penetrate. He

therefore persuaded Baugi to bore a hole through the rock, which he had no sooner done than Odin, transforming himself into a worm, crept through the crevice, and resuming his natural shape, won the heart of Gunnlauth. After passing three nights with the fair maiden, he had no great difficulty in inducing her to let him take a draught out of each of the three jars, called Odhroerir, Bodn, and Son, in which the mead was kept. But wishing to make the most of his advantage, he pulled so deep that not a drop was left in the vessels. Transforming himself into an eagle, he then flew off as fast as his wings could carry him, but Suttung becoming aware of the stratagem, also took upon himself an eagle's guise, and flew after him. The Æsir, on seeing him approach Asgard, set out in the yard all the jars they could lay their hands on, which Odin filled by discharging through his beak the wonder-working liquor he had drunk. He was however, so near being caught by Suttung, that some of the liquor escaped him by an impurer vent, and as no care was taken of this it fell to the share of the poetasters. But the liquor discharged in the jars was kept for the gods, and for those men who have sufficient wit to make a right use of it. Hence poetry is also called Odin's booty, Odin's gift, the beverage of the gods, &c, &c.

FOOTNOTES:

[Footnote 125: This chapter is probably the interpolation of an early copyist, for it has evidently no connection with the following one, and is not found in the Upsal MS. of the Prose Edda, which is supposed to be the oldest extant. Gefjon's ploughing is obviously a mythic way of accounting for some convulsions of nature, perhaps the convulsion that produced the Sound, and thus effected a junction between the Baltic and the Northern Ocean.]

[Footnote 126: Rime Giants, or Giants of the Frost.]

[Footnote 127: Literally, "It is light and hot, insomuch so that it is flaming and burning, and it is impervious to those who are outlandish (foreign), and not indigenous there" (or who have no home or heritage therein).]

[Footnote 128: More properly speaking, to the earth which it encircled.]

[Footnote 129: A ferreous or glacial refrigeration.]

[Footnote 130: _i.e._ If Thor drove over Bifrost with his thunder chariot.]

[Footnote 131: _i.e._ Present, Past, and Future.]

[Footnote 132: Namely, his having killed Baldur.]

[Footnote 133: Mind or Thought, and Memory.]

[Footnote 134: _i.e._ Devouring flame.]

[Footnote 135: _i.e._ Spirit or thought.]

[Footnote 136: _i.e._ Eld or Old Age.]

[Footnote 137: Finn Magnusen's explanation of this myth is, that Iduna--the ever-renovating Spring--being in the possession of Thjassi--the desolating winter--all nature languishes until she is delivered from her captivity. On this being effected, her presence again diffuses joy and gladness, and all things revive; while her pursuer, Winter, with his icy breath, dissolves in the solar rays indicated by the fires lighted on the walls of Asgard.]

ᛏᛟᛏᛗᛊ

NOTES

ᚾᛟᛏᛖᛊ

NOTES

TOTEMS

TOTEMS

TOTMS

NOTES

ᛏᛟᛏᛗᛊ

ᚺᛟᛏᛖᛋ

Made in the USA
Monee, IL
09 September 2023

42441867R00052